Amazing Angels Activity Book

ARCTURUS

ARCTURUS

This edition published in 2019 by Arcturus Publishing Limited
26/27 Bickels Yard, 151–153 Bermondsey Street,
London SE1 3HA

Author: Lisa Regan
Illustrator: Sam Loman
Editor: Becca Clunes
Designer: Well Nice Ltd.

ISBN: 978-1-78950-251-0
CH006972NT
Supplier 29, Date 0519, Print run 8118

Printed in China

Shimmer and Shine

Which of the sparkling stars is slightly different from the others?

Not Quite Perfect!

Unscramble the letters to make angel words for each halo.

1. HOAL

2. GWINS

3. CAPEE

4. VLOE

5. THLIG

Four Seasons

Match each of the angels of the seasons to the correct silhouette.

Something's Wrong

Can you find three things that
are wrong in this picture?

Dear Little Deers

Trace over each of the animals to learn
how to draw them for yourself.

Little Cherubs

Which of these cherubs is called Vincent?
Work it out using the clues.

A

B

C

D

1. He is holding something.

2. He is wearing pink.

3. His eyes are open.

8

Your Turn

Learn how to draw an angel by following the steps.

Sent From Above

What two characteristics should an angel have?
Cross out or shade in all of the squares containing
O, H, or L, and the remaining letters will show you.

O	H	O	L	H	O	H	O	L	H
L	G	H	L	R	O	A	L	H	O
H	L	H	H	L	H	O	O	L	L
L	O	O	C	H	E	H	L	L	H
L	K	L	O	I	O	H	O	H	O
H	L	H	L	O	N	L	L	H	L
L	O	O	H	L	O	D	L	H	O
H	L	N	L	E	L	O	O	O	H
L	O	O	L	H	S	O	L	H	L
O	H	L	O	L	O	L	H	S	O

Sweet Harmony

Which of the characters is playing a different tune?

Picnic Party

Can you spot eight differences between these two perfect picnics?

Night Sky

Use your pens or crayons to bring this scene to life!

Secret Message

Do you speak angel? You can now, with the help of the angel decoder below. What is she saying?

☆ ✛ ✿ ✚ ✛   ✿ ★ ✤   ★ ✦ ✳ ✛

_ _ _ _ _   _ _ _   _ _ _ _

✳ ✦   ✛ ✦ ✛ ✳ ⬡ ✦ ✦ ✛ ⬢

_ _   _ _ _ _ _ _ _ _ _

A = ✿	F = ✦	K = ☆	P = ☆	U = ✳	Z = ✺
B = ✛	G = ✧	L = ✦	Q = ✳	V = ✦	! = ✷
C = ✚	H = ★	M = ✿	R = ✳	W = ✿	? = ✿
D = ✛	I = ☆	N = ✦	S = ✳	X = ✦	, = ◎
E = ✛	J = ✪	O = ✦	T = ✳	Y = ⬡	. = ⬢

An Angel Calls

Find the quickest way for the angel to visit each of the houses just once, without crossing over a path she has already taken.

Lost and Found

Portia has lost her diary! Can you help her to find it?
It is green with a purple heart on it.

Spiral Saying

Starting with the "F," write down every other letter on the answer lines. Then return to the start and write the remaining letters to complete the message.

A F L L A L N E G N E F L E I A S T W H A E T R C S H L I E N T G Y N R K E U V O O Y O O W U

F _ _ _ _ _   _ _ _ _ _ _ _   _ _ _   _ _ _   _ _ _ _   _ _

_ _ _ _ _   _ _   _ _ _ _ _ _ _ _   _ _ _ _   _ _ _

17

Heavenly Music

The angels are late for music practice.
Can you help find an instrument for each of them?

Your Turn

Here are some of the things an angel might carry.
Can you draw them?

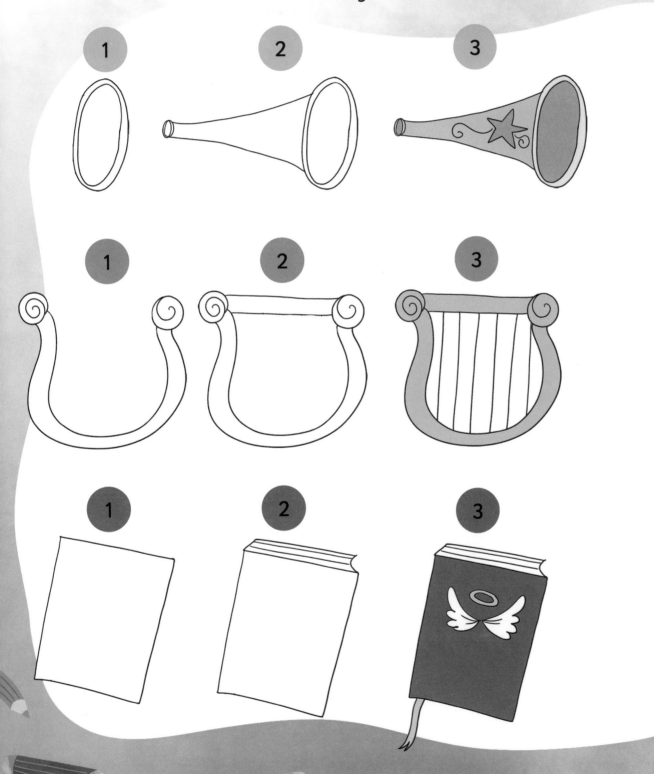

What's the Weather?

Angels love hot days, but they have to cope with the rain, just like we do! Unscramble the weather words and match them to the correct picture.

NYWID

ROOMSTNWS

GRIANNI

HISNUNSE

Perfect Pet

What shape is hiding in the grid? It is the animal that Ariadne loves the most! Shade in the shapes that contain a 1 to find it.

Rise and Shine

How many new words, containing three or more letters,
can you make out of the phrase here?

ANGEL OF THE
MORNING

- - - - - - - - - - - - - -   - - - - - - - - - - - - -

- - - - - - - - - - - - - -   - - - - - - - - - - - - -

- - - - - - - - - - - - - -   - - - - - - - - - - - - -

- - - - - - - - - - - - - -   - - - - - - - - - - - - -

- - - - - - - - - - - - - -   - - - - - - - - - - - - -

Reunited

Find a way through the clouds to reunite the angel friends.

START

FINISH

23

Loving Words

Rearrange the letters on the hearts and work out which heart does not spell the word "loving."

1 GILOVN

2 GLOVIN

3 INLOVG

4 LONGVI

5 LOVGIN

6 NLOVIN

7 GINLOV

Angels with Dirty Laundry

Match the socks into pairs, then circle the sock which is left over on each washing line.

All Together

The angels are having such fun playing together! Can you find each of the named angels, using the clues?

Sophia is smelling a flower.

Erin is petting a duckling.

Tristan is sleeping.

26

27

Heavenly Music

Use the clues to work out which angel is which, and then match them to the correct musical instrument.

	Pipe	Harp	Lute
Beatrice			
Amy			
Clara			

	Beatrice	Amy	Clara
Pink wings			
Blue wings			
Yellow wings			

Clues

1. Amy does not have pink wings.

2. Clara doesn't play the lute.

3. The person who plays the pipe has yellow wings.

4. Beatrice plays the harp.

28

More Music!

Fill the page with more beautiful musical doodling.

Words of Wisdom

Can you find each of the listed words hidden in the grid?

KINDNESS   **PEACE**   **JOY**   **SHARING**   **HELPFUL**
WISDOM   **LOVE**   **LIGHT**   **SYMPATHY**   **CARING**

J	O	W	E	O	J	E	T	S	T	H	Y
S	P	S	I	O	O	H	M	Y	H	S	L
H	D	E	E	S	G	E	O	M	Y	H	O
A	K	T	A	I	D	L	V	P	H	A	V
R	I	M	L	W	H	O	A	A	E	R	E
H	N	Y	K	I	N	Y	M	T	L	K	J
E	D	S	H	A	R	T	G	H	P	I	O
L	N	J	R	E	E	O	H	Y	F	N	H
P	E	O	J	C	T	V	T	S	U	N	E
E	S	Y	A	H	K	I	N	W	L	A	L
A	S	E	I	Y	S	H	A	R	I	N	G
T	P	I	W	O	V	E	I	G	H	T	H
H	T	C	A	R	I	N	G	A	T	H	Y

It All Adds Up

How many acts of kindness has each angel carried out today?
Add up the symbols on each scroll using the number code below.

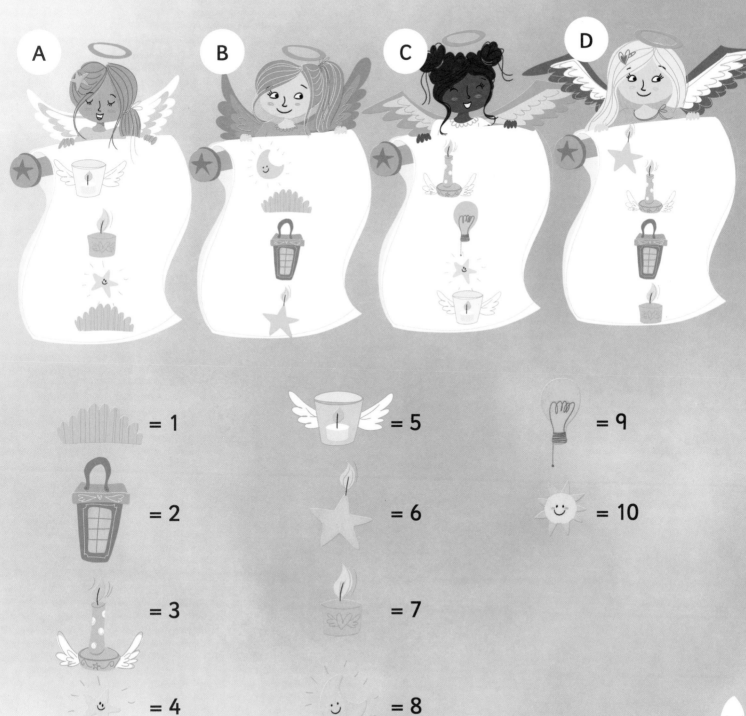

Snow Angels!

Which one of the jigsaw pieces fits into the puzzle?

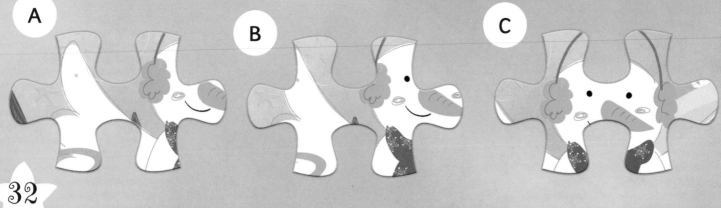

A   B   C

Happy Thoughts

See how many times you can find the word ANGEL hidden in this grid.
Look from left to right, and from top to bottom.

A	N	G	L	E	N	G	A	L	E	L	E	A	N	G
G	A	N	N	A	L	A	N	G	N	A	G	N	A	L
L	N	A	N	L	L	E	G	A	N	G	E	L	N	N
E	A	G	G	E	E	A	L	N	G	G	A	E	L	A
E	G	N	A	G	A	N	L	L	E	L	N	G	N	N
A	A	G	E	L	E	G	E	G	L	E	G	L	E	G
N	N	A	N	G	A	L	A	E	N	E	E	E	A	L
G	G	N	A	N	L	G	N	G	N	A	L	A	N	E
L	E	G	N	L	E	E	L	L	E	N	G	L	E	A
E	L	G	E	N	A	N	G	E	L	A	G	N	E	E

33

Doves From Above

How many white doves holding pink flowers can you see in the scene?

Matchmaking

Which of the silhouettes is an exact match for the angel in the middle?

Gridlocked

Aaliyah is struggling to deliver her message to the house below. Find a path through the trumpets, going only in this direction along a trumpet:

START

FINISH

Let It Snow
Which snowflake is one of a kind?

Getting the Message

Angels can leave messages in mysterious ways.
What does this one say?

___   ___   ___   ___   ___

 RECEIVING ALWAYS BUT LOVE

 GIVING YOU HAPPY FEEL

 WANTING ME BEST DOES

 WHEN SO MAKES

Sleeping Beauties

Use the grid lines to help you copy
this sleepy little angel and her friend.

While They Play

The angels watch over all the newborns while they play. Can you spot ten differences between the two scenes?

Here I Am

How would you feel if an angel is near? Shade in all of the squares containing U, G, or D, and the remaining letters will spell two words that show you.

G	D	U	G	G	D	U	G	G	D
D	U	D	D	U	D	G	D	D	U
U	G	D	U	G	D	U	G	D	U
G	D	U	U	D	U	G	U	G	G
U	G	J	G	O	G	D	G	Y	D
D	D	U	D	U	D	U	G	D	U
G	D	G	U	U	G	D	U	G	U
U	P	D	E	U	G	D	U	D	D
D	G	D	U	A	G	U	G	U	U
G	D	U	D	D	U	C	D	E	G

42

Gift Giving

Which of the Christmas angels is the odd one out?

Ding Dong Merrily

Which angel is ringing which bell?
Follow the cords to find out.

Puppy Love

Can you match each angel to their perfect pet?
Each angel has something in common with their pet.

Wish Upon a Star

If you see an extra-twinkly star, it may be an angel that
will grant you a wish. Can you spot the six-pointed star in this sky?

Guardian Angels

Finish this picture with your pens, pencils, or crayons.

Shining Bright

If each section of a candle burns for five minutes,
which of the candles will burn for half an hour?

Spiral Saying

Starting with the "A," write down every other letter on the answer lines. Then return to the start and write the remaining letters to complete the message.

A _ _ _ _ _ _ _   _ _ _   _ _ _ _ _ _ _ _ _ _   _ _ _ _

_ _ _ _ _   _ _ _ _ _ _   _ _   _ _ _ _ _

Your Turn

Learn how to draw a cute cherub by following the steps.

Hidden Gems

What shape is hiding in the grid? It is Alexa's prize possession!
Shade in the shapes that contain a 1 to find it.

Healthy Harvest

The harvest angel has more fruit than she can eat!
How many of each type can you count in her basket?

Watching Over You

Do you have a guardian angel? Use the first letter of your name and the month you were born to work it out. So if you are called Lisa and were born in July, your angel will be Asta the Wise.

A, J, S = VIRGIL

D, M, V = JERA

G, P, Y = VIDIS

B, K, T = SHARI

E, N, W = TATIANA

H, Q, Z = MISHA

C, L, U = ASTA

F, O, X = JACOB

I, R = ARIANA

JANUARY = THE THOUGHTFUL

JULY = THE WISE

FEBRUARY = THE JOYFUL

AUGUST = THE BENEVOLENT

MARCH = THE GENTLE

SEPTEMBER = THE NOBLE

APRIL = THE MERCIFUL

OCTOBER = THE KINDLY

MAY = THE HELPFUL

NOVEMBER = THE GENEROUS

JUNE = THE PLAYFUL

DECEMBER = THE BRAVE

My guardian angel is called

Rise and Shine

How many new words, containing three or more letters, can you make out of the phrase here?

COUNT YOUR BLESSINGS

----------------   ----------------

----------------   ----------------

----------------   ----------------

----------------   ----------------

----------------   ----------------

----------------   ----------------

A-maze-ing!

Can you find a way through this musical maze?

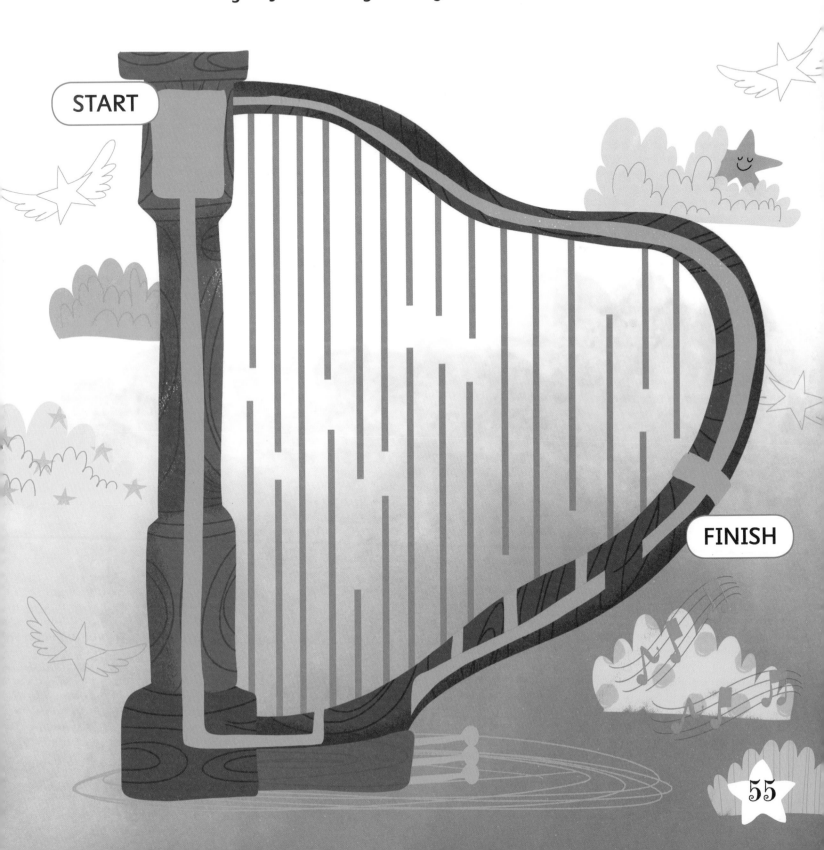

START

FINISH

55

Angel Wishes

What would you wish for if an angel could grant your wishes?
Using the secret code, work out what these wishes say.

I wish I could ...

1

SZEV Z KVG
FMRXLIM

2

YV ZM
ZHGILMZFG

3

URMW YFIRVW
GIVZHFIV

A = Z	E = V	I = R	M = N	Q = J	U = F	Y = B
B = Y	F = U	J = Q	N = M	R = I	V = E	Z = A
C = X	G = T	K = P	O = L	S = H	W = D	
D = W	H = S	L = O	P = K	T = G	X = C	

A Special Gift
Which of the silhouettes is an exact match for the picture in the middle?

A

B

C

D

Rhyme Time

How good at rhyming are you? See if you can list five words to rhyme with each of the words on the angel wings.

LIGHT

KIND

PEACE

JOY

Angel Heart

How many heart shapes can you count in this picture? Finish it with your pens and crayons once you have counted.

Making Music

Look carefully to find all of the musical words hidden in the grid.

CHOIR　　**SOPRANO**　　**CHORUS**　　**TRUMPET**　　**FLUTE**
HARMONY　　**CAROL**　　**VIOLIN**　　**HARP**　　**PIANO**

H	F	T	R	U	M	C	L	S	V	C	T
V	A	L	I	O	P	H	F	O	I	H	R
I	Y	H	N	V	I	O	L	P	A	O	U
D	D	A	B	C	H	O	I	R	V	V	M
O	I	R	O	C	A	Y	P	I	I	C	F
P	A	M	T	H	A	R	M	E	O	A	L
V	E	O	N	R	D	F	O	Y	L	R	U
T	P	N	P	I	U	M	L	L	I	L	T
R	O	Y	S	O	A	M	H	U	N	I	E
U	T	H	A	R	S	O	P	R	A	N	O
M	C	A	R	H	C	H	O	E	C	A	R
S	C	H	O	R	U	S	P	I	T	T	T
P	I	A	I	R	T	R	U	M	L	E	C

Lots of Love

Fill the page with more angels, clouds, and hearts.

Secret Message

Decode the message to find out what the angel has to tell you.

A = ✿	F = ✦	K = ☆	P = ☆	U = ✳	Z = ✳
B = ✛	G = ◇	L = ✩	Q = ✳	V = ✳	! = ✳
C = ✤	H = ★	M = ✾	R = ✳	W = ✺	? = ✿
D = ✤	I = ☆	N = ✩	S = ✳	X = ✳	, = ◎
E = ✤	J = ✪	O = ✭	T = ✳	Y = ✿	. = ✿

_ _ _ _ _ _ _   _ _ _   _ _ _ _ _ _   _ _

_ _ _ _ _ _ _ _   _ _ _ _ _ _ _ _   _ _ _   _ _ _

On Cloud Nine

Work out the answers to find out which angel is, literally, on cloud nine!

A $18 \div 3$

B $24 \div 8$

C $48 \div 6$

D $28 \div 4$

E $16 \div 2$

F $56 \div 7$

G $45 \div 5$

H $32 \div 4$

I $21 \div 3$

63

Superstars

Look carefully to find ten differences between these two pictures.

Getting It Wrong

Angels don't always get things right! Add up the points of the items on their scrolls. Which of them has written the wrong answer?

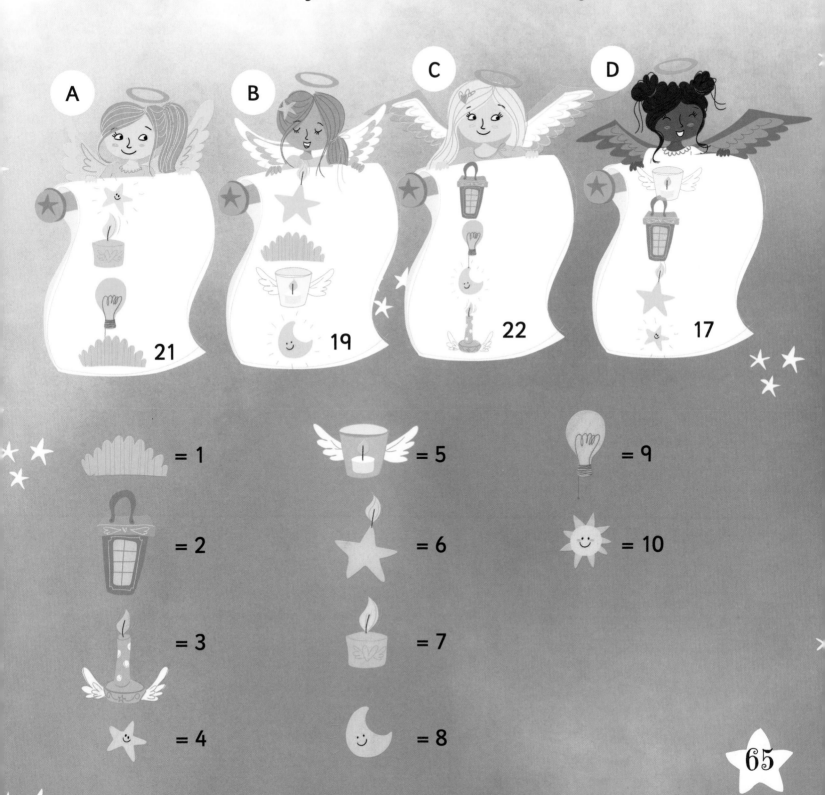

A   21

B   19

C   22

D   17

= 1

= 2

= 3

= 4

= 5

= 6

= 7

= 8

= 9

= 10

Fun With Friends

How many of each of the items in the circles can you count in this scene?

67

Bugle Call

Find five angel words hidden in the string of letters.
The remaining letters spell the name of this angel.

Which Wings?

If you were a guardian angel, what would your wings look like? Follow the instructions below to find out.

1. Write out your full name.

2. Count the number of letters in it.

3. If your answer is more than 9, add together the digits to make a single number.

4. Now check out which pair of wings is yours!

Flower Power

Can you fill in this sudoku grid? Each row, column, and small box should have one of each type of flower.
Here are the six flowers that are used in the puzzle:

Season's Greetings

Trace over this tree and its decorations so you can learn how to draw them for yourself.

Flying High

Which one of the jigsaw pieces doesn't fit into the puzzle?

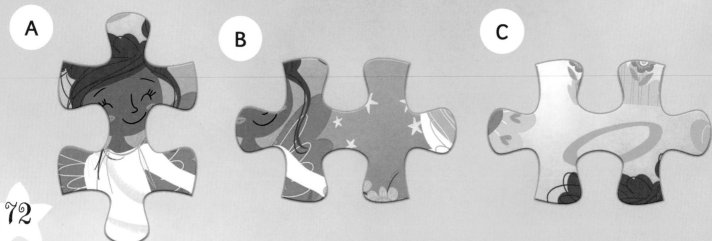

A

B

C

Spiral Saying

Starting with the "M," write down every other letter on the answer lines. Then return to the start and write the remaining letters to complete the message.

M___ ____ _____ __ _____

____ ___ _____ __ _____

At Your Service

Cross out or shade in all of the squares containing M, F or B.
The remaining letters will show you two things that an angel can give you.

M	B	B	M	P	R	M	F	B	M
M	F	M	B	F	M	O	F	F	B
F	T	F	E	F	B	B	M	B	M
B	M	F	B	F	C	F	T	F	F
M	B	I	M	O	M	N	M	B	B
M	B	F	B	M	B	F	F	M	B
F	G	F	U	F	M	B	I	B	M
B	F	M	B	D	A	B	M	B	F
M	B	N	M	M	F	M	F	C	B
B	F	M	F	B	B	E	B	M	F

74

Feathered Friends

Which two of these beautiful swans match each other exactly?

I Spy

Use your powers of perception to find the four mini-pictures somewhere in this scene.

76

77

Greetings!

How many new words, containing three or more letters, can you make out of the phrase here?

GOOD TIDINGS

Gorgeous Garland

Bring this beautiful scene to life with your pens and crayons.

Yummy Scrummy!

Which are there more of, cherries or strawberries?

Hoppity Skip

Add some more magic to this scene.

Pretty Patterns

The angels are putting up decorations, but some bits are missing.
Study the sequence of shapes, and fill in the gaps.

Your Turn

Learn how to draw a unicorn by following the steps.

Shining Bright

How many words linked to "light" can you find in the grid?
There are 10 to find! Look across and down.

L	U	S	L	F	B	R	S	N	G	L
F	G	U	Z	M	O	O	N	L	L	I
L	B	N	O	O	A	O	T	Z	O	L
A	R	S	T	T	M	O	T	Z	W	G
S	I	S	P	A	R	K	L	E	I	L
H	L	T	W	B	R	A	Z	Z	N	I
L	L	U	M	I	N	O	U	S	G	T
L	I	O	O	G	N	S	G	L	A	T
D	A	Z	Z	L	E	T	N	L	Z	E
S	N	S	H	S	T	A	N	S	Z	R
T	T	T	H	T	S	R	I	G	H	S

84

Magical Maze

Find a way through the rainbow maze, without getting zapped by lightning along the way.

START

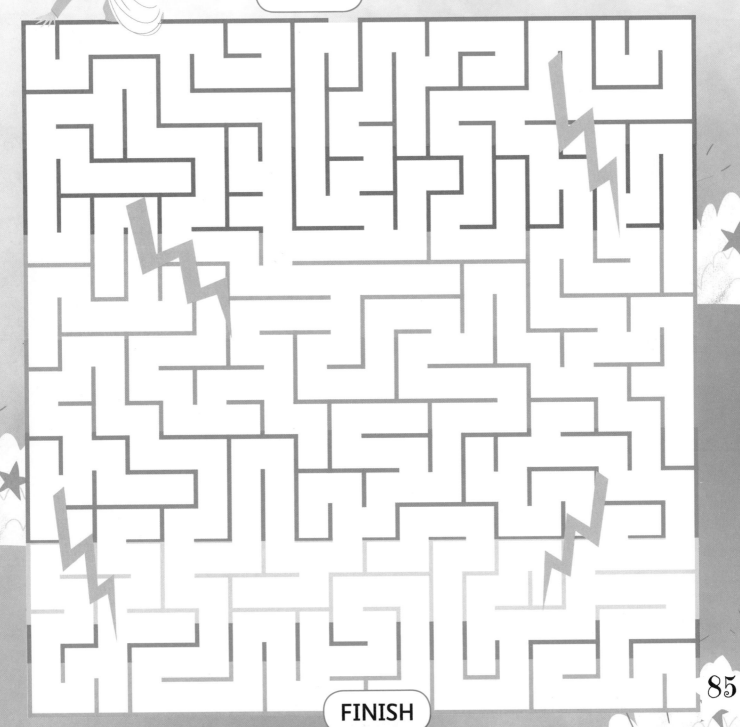

FINISH

85

Getting the Message

Angels can leave messages in mysterious ways.
What does this one say?

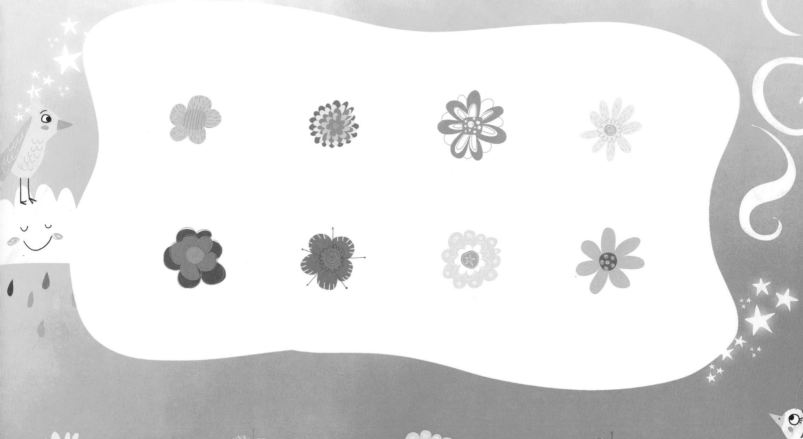

 CARING THINK KIND DO

 ANGELS ARE HAPPY THINGS

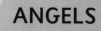 TIME YOU WHEN

 86

Star Light, Star Bright

See if you can spot this constellation somewhere in the starry sky.

Floral Flaw

Fleur has been making beautiful garlands, but she has got one slightly wrong. Which one needs to be made again?

Answers

Page 3

Page 4

The words are:

1 = HALO

2 = WINGS

3 = PEACE

4 = LOVE

5 = LIGHT

Page 5

Answer:
A = 2
B = 1
C = 4
D = 3

Page 6

Page 8

Answer: A

Page 10

O	H	O	L	H	O	H	O	L	H
L	G	H	L	R	O	A	L	H	O
H	L	H	H	L	H	O	O	L	L
L	O	O	C	H	E	H	L	L	H
L	K	L	O	I	O	H	O	H	O
H	L	H	L	O	N	L	L	H	L
L	O	O	H	L	O	D	L	H	O
H	L	N	L	E	L	O	O	O	H
L	O	O	L	H	S	O	L	H	L
O	H	L	O	L	O	L	H	S	O

Answer: GRACE, KINDNESS

Page 11

Page 12

Page 14

Answer: PEACE AND LOVE TO EVERYONE.

Answers

Page 15

Page 16

Page 17

Answer:

FALLEN FEATHERS LET YOU KNOW AN ANGEL IS WATCHING OVER YOU.

Page 18

Page 20

Answers:

WINDY

SNOWSTORM

RAINING

SUNSHINE

Page 21

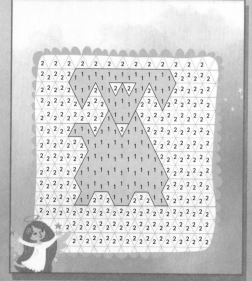

Answer: A DOG

Page 22

Here are some you can make:

Long, gnome, gentle, melon, grin, month, nothing, egg, men, lighten, ten, night, leg.

Page 23

Answers

Page 24

Answer: 6

Page 25

Page 28

	Pipe	Harp	Lute
Beatrice		X	
Amy			X
Clara	X		

	Beatrice	Amy	Clara
Pink wings	X		
Blue wings		X	
Yellow wings			X

Pages 26-27

Sophia
Erin
Tristan
Helga
Jerome
Amos
Lois

Page 30

```
J O W E O J E T S T H Y
S P S I O O H M Y H S L
H D E E S G E O M Y H O
A K T A I D L V P H A V
R I M L W H O A A E R E
H N Y K I N Y M T L K J
E D S H A R T G H P I O
L N J R E E O H Y F N H
P E O J C T V T S U N E
E S Y A H K I N W L A L
A S E I Y S H A R I N G
T P I W O V E I G H T H
H T C A R I N G A T H Y
```

Page 31

Answer:

A = 17, B = 17, C = 21, D = 18

Page 32

Answer: C

Answers

Page 33

A	N	G	L	E	N	G	A	L	E	L	E	A	N	G
G	A	N	N	A	L	A	N	G	N	A	G	N	A	L
L	N	A	N	L	L	E	G	A	N	G	E	L	N	N
E	A	G	G	E	E	A	L	N	G	G	A	E	L	A
E	G	N	A	G	A	N	L	L	E	L	N	G	N	N
A	A	G	E	L	E	G	E	G	L	E	G	L	E	G
N	N	A	N	G	A	L	A	E	N	E	E	E	A	L
G	G	N	A	N	L	G	N	G	N	A	L	A	N	E
L	E	G	N	L	E	E	L	L	E	N	G	L	E	A
E	L	G	E	N	A	N	G	E	L	A	G	N	E	E

Answer: 4

Page 34

Answer: 3

Page 35

Page 36

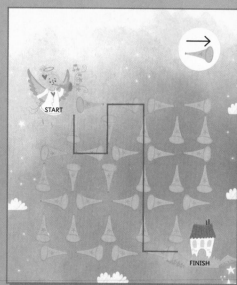

Page 37

Page 38

Answer: GIVING LOVE MAKES ME HAPPY.

Pages 40-41

92

Answers

Page 42

G	D	U	G	G	D	U	G	G	D
D	U	D	D	U	D	G	D	D	U
U	G	D	U	G	D	U	G	D	U
G	D	U	U	D	U	G	U	G	G
U	G	J	G	O	G	D	G	Y	D
D	D	U	D	U	D	U	G	D	U
G	D	G	U	U	G	D	U	G	U
U	P	D	E	U	G	D	U	D	D
D	G	D	U	A	G	U	G	U	U
G	D	U	D	D	U	C	D	E	G

Answer: JOY, PEACE.

Page 44

Page 46

Page 43

Page 45

Page 48

Answer: D

Page 49

Answer: ANGELS ARE SUPERHEROES WITH WINGS INSTEAD OF CAPES.

Answers

Page 51

Answer: A CROWN

Page 52

Page 54

Here are some you can make: Glossy, run, slug, citrus, soon, long, only, song, sunny, rung, tiny, snout, turn, cousin, noisy.

Page 55

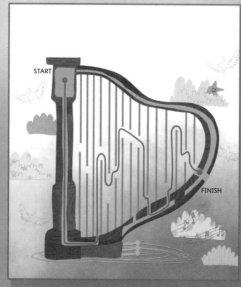

Page 56

Answer: Coded messages

1 = HAVE A PET UNICORN

2 = BE AN ASTRONAUT

3 = FIND BURIED TREASURE

Page 57

Page 58

Here are some you might have thought of:

LIGHT: night/knight, kite, right/write, white, flight

KIND: find, behind, blind, signed, mind

PEACE: geese, fleece, niece, grease/Greece, crease

JOY: boy, toy, enjoy, soy, ploy

Page 59

Answer: 18